Assessment Guide
Grade 2

Houghton
Mifflin
Harcourt

INCLUDES:

- Prerequisite Skills Inventory
- Beginning-of-Year, Middle-of-Year, and End-of-Year Tests
- Chapter Tests
- Performance Tasks
- Getting Ready for Grade 3 Tests
- Individual Record Forms

Contents

Tests and Record Forms

Overview of Florida *Go Math!* Assessment

How Assessment Can Help Individualize Instruction

The *Assessment Guide* contains several types of assessment for use throughout the school year. The following pages will explain how these assessments can help teachers evaluate children's understanding of the standards. This Assessment Guide also contains Individual Record Forms to help guide teachers' instructional choices and to improve children's performance.

Diagnostic Assessment

Prerequisite Skills Inventory in the *Assessment Guide* should be given at the beginning of the year or when a new child arrives. This short-answer test yields insight regarding understanding of prerequisite skills. Test results provide information about the review or intervention that children may need in order to be successful in the coming year. Suggestions for intervention are provided for this inventory.

Beginning-of-Year Test in the *Assessment Guide* is multiple-choice format and should be utilized early in the year to establish on-grade-level skills children may already understand. This benchmark test will allow customization of instructional content to optimize the time spent teaching specific objectives. Suggestions for intervention are provided for this test.

Show What You Know in the *Student Edition* is provided for each chapter. It assesses prior knowledge from previous grades as well as content taught earlier in the current grade. Teachers can customize instructional content using the intervention options provided. The assessment should be scheduled at the beginning of each chapter to determine if children have the prerequisite skills.

Diagnostic Interview Assessment in the *Teacher Edition* and *Assessment Guide* is designed to provide an optional instrument to evaluate each child's level of accomplishment for the chapter's prerequisite skills on the **Show What You Know**. The interview task items test children at the concrete or pictorial level where appropriate.

Formative Assessment

Lesson Quick Check in every lesson of the *Teacher Edition* monitors children's understanding of the skills and concepts being presented.

Standards Practice for every lesson in the *Standards Practice Book* helps children achieve fluency, speed, and confidence with grade level skills and concepts.

Mid-Chapter Checkpoint in the *Student Edition* provides monitoring of children's progress to permit instructional adjustments, and when required, to facilitate children's mastery of the objectives.

Middle-of-Year Test in the *Assessment Guide* assesses the same standards as the Beginning-of-Year Test, allowing children's progress to be tracked and providing opportunity for instructional adjustments, when required.

Portfolios encourage children to collect work samples throughout the chapter as a reinforcement of their progress and achievements.

Summative Assessment

Chapter Review/Tests in the *Student Edition* indicate whether additional instruction or practice is necessary for children to master the concepts and skills taught in the chapter. These tests include items presented in a variety of assessment formats.

Chapter Tests in the *Assessment Guide* evaluate children's mastery of concepts and skills taught in the chapter. These tests assess the mastery of Mathematics Florida Standards taught in a chapter. Item types on these tests are similar to ones a child would encounter on a test to assess Mathematics Florida Standards.

Performance Tasks in the *Assessment Guide* are provided for each Chapter and Unit. Each assessment contains several tasks to assess children's ability to use what they have learned and provides an opportunity for children to display their thinking strategies. Each set of tasks is accompanied by teacher support pages, a rubric for scoring, and examples of student work for the task.

End-of-Year Tests in the *Assessment Guide* assess the same standards as the Beginning- and Middle-of-Year Tests. It is the final benchmark test for the grade level. When children's performance on the End-of-Year Test is compared to performance on the Beginning- and Middle-of-Year Tests, teachers are able to document children's growth.

Getting Ready Tests in the *Assessment Guide* evaluate the children's understanding of concepts and skills taught as readiness for the next grade level. These tests are available in a mixed-response format comprised of multiple choice and short answer.

Data-Driven Decision Making

Go Math! allows for quick and accurate data-driven decision making so the teacher can spend more instructional time tailoring to children's needs. The **Data-Driven Decision Making** chart with Diagnostic, Formative, and Summative Assessments provides prescribed interventions so children have a greater opportunity for success with Mathematics Florida Standards.

Intervention and Review Resources

For skills that children have not yet mastered, the Reteach activities in *Reteach* or Tier 1 and Tier 2 RtI Activities online provide additional instruction and practice on concepts and skills in the chapter.

Using Individual Record Forms

The *Assessment Guide* includes Individual Record Forms (IRF) for all tests. On these forms, each test item is correlated to the standard it assesses. There are intervention resources correlated to each item as well. A common error explains why a child may have missed the item. These forms can be used to:

- Follow progress throughout the year.
- Identify strengths, weaknesses, and provide follow-up instruction.
- Make assignments based on the intervention options provided.

Performance Assessment

Performance Assessment, together with other types of assessment, can supply the missing information not provided by other testing formats. Performance Tasks, in particular, help reveal the thinking strategies children use to work through a problem. Performance Tasks with multiple tasks for each chapter and Unit are provided in the *Assessment Guide*.

Each of these assessments has several tasks that target specific math concepts, skills, and strategies. These tasks can help assess children's ability to use what they have learned to solve everyday problems. Each assessment focuses on a theme. Teachers can plan for children to complete one task at a time or use an extended amount of time to complete the entire assessment.

Teacher support pages accompany each Performance Task. A task-specific rubric helps teachers evaluate children's work. Papers to illustrate actual children's work are also provided to aid in scoring.

Portfolio Assessment

A portfolio is a collection of each child's work gathered over an extended period of time.

A portfolio illustrates the growth, talents, achievements, and reflections of the learner and provides a means for you and the child to assess performance and progress.

Building a Portfolio

There are many opportunities to collect children's work throughout the year as you use *Go Math!* Give children the opportunity to select some work samples to be included in the portfolio.

- Provide a folder for each child with the child's name clearly marked.
- Explain to children that throughout the year they will save some of their work in the folder. Sometimes it will be their individual work; sometimes it will be group reports and projects or completed checklists.

Evaluating a Portfolio

The following points made with regular portfolio evaluation will encourage growth in self-evaluation:

- Discuss the contents of the portfolio as you examine it with each child.
- Encourage and reward each child by emphasizing growth, original thinking, and completion of tasks.
- Reinforce and adjust instruction of the broad goals you want to accomplish as you evaluate the portfolios.
- Examine each portfolio on the basis of individual growth rather than in comparison with other portfolios.
- Share the portfolio with family during conferences or send the portfolio home with the child.

Assessment Formats

The assessments in the *Assessment Guide* contain item types beyond the traditional multiple-choice format. This variety allows for a more robust assessment of children's understanding of concepts. The following information is provided to help teachers familiarize children with these different types of items. You may want to use the examples to introduce the item types to children. The following explanations are provided to guide children in answering the questions. These pages describe the most common item types. You may find other types on some tests.

Example 1 Tell if a number matches another representation.

Yes or No

For this type of item, children respond to a single question with several examples. There will be a question and children will fill in the bubble next to "Yes" or "No" to answer each part. They must fill in a bubble for each part.

Example 2 Choose numbers less than a given number.

More Than One Correct Choice

This type of item may confuse children because it looks like a traditional multiple-choice item. Tell children this type of item will ask them to choose all of something. Explain that when the item asks them to find all, they should look for more than one correct choice. Tell them to carefully look at each choice and mark it if it is a correct answer.

Example 3 Choose tens and ones to describe a number.

Choose From a List

Sometimes when children take a test on a computer, they will have to select a word, number, or symbol from a drop-down list. The *Go Math!* tests show a list and ask children to choose the correct answer. Tell children to make their choice by circling the correct answer. There will only be one choice that is correct.

Choose the correct answer.

1. Which shows a related addition fact?

$$15 - 8 = 7$$

- ○ $15 + 7 = 22$
- ○ $8 - 7 = 1$
- ○ $7 + 8 = 15$
- ○ $23 - 8 = 15$

2. There are 9 bugs on the grass and 5 bugs on a leaf. Which number sentence shows how many bugs there are in all?

- ○ $10 + 5 = 15$
- ○ $9 + 5 = 14$
- ○ $9 - 5 = 4$
- ○ $5 + 4 = 9$

3. Gina has 4 green trains, 2 red trains, and 6 yellow trains. How many trains does Gina have in all?

- ○ 6
- ○ 8
- ○ 10
- ○ 12

4. There are 725 students in the school. There are 343 boys. How many girls are there?

Hundreds	Tens	Ones
☐	☐	☐
7	2	5
− 3	4	3

- ○ 382
- ○ 422
- ○ 428
- ○ 482

GO ON ➡

5. What is the sum?

$$378$$
$$+\ 215$$

○ 163   ○ 593

○ 583   ○ 693

6. What is the difference?

$$402$$
$$-\ 173$$

○ 339   ○ 329

○ 331   ○ 229

7. Use an inch ruler. What is the length of the ribbon to the nearest inch?

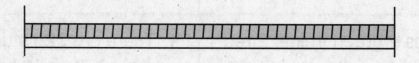

○ 8 inches   ○ 4 inches

○ 6 inches   ○ 2 inches

8. Use the line plot.
How many toy cars are 3 inches long?

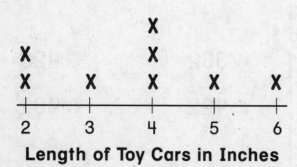

Length of Toy Cars in Inches

○ 1

○ 2

○ 3

○ 4

GO ON

9. Which is the **best** estimate of the length of a baseball bat?

- ○ 2 feet
- ○ 6 feet
- ○ 8 feet
- ○ 10 feet

10. Fred wants to measure the distance around a ball. Which is the **best** tool for Fred to use?

- ○ counters
- ○ cup
- ○ measuring tape
- ○ pencil

11. Ms. Angeles writes an odd number on the board. Which could be the number that Ms. Angeles writes?

- ○ 3
- ○ 4
- ○ 6
- ○ 8

12. What is the value of the underlined digit?

<u>3</u>8

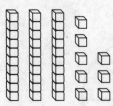

- ○ 3
- ○ 8
- ○ 30
- ○ 80

GO ON

13. Which shows another way to write the number?

57

○ 7 tens 5 ones

○ fifty-seven

○ 5 + 7

○ 5 + 70

14. Which group of numbers shows counting by hundreds?

○ 300, 310, 320, 330

○ 400, 401, 402, 403

○ 500, 600, 700, 800

○ 600, 605, 610, 615

15. Which object is shaped like a cylinder?

○

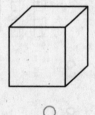
○

16. Which names a shape with 4 sides and 4 vertices?

○ triangle

○ quadrilateral

○ pentagon

○ hexagon

GO ON

17. Which of these shapes has **fewer** than 4 angles?

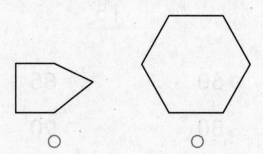

○   ○

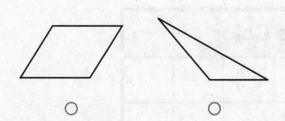

○   ○

18. Which shows a half of the shape shaded?

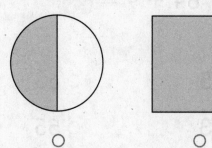

○   ○

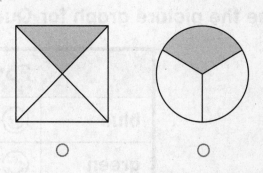

○   ○

19. Which number will make this number sentence true?

$$14 - 5 = \boxed{} + 4$$

○ 2

○ 3

○ 5

○ 7

20. What is the sum?

$$\begin{array}{r} 24 \\ 15 \\ + \ 36 \\ \hline \end{array}$$

○ 75

○ 65

○ 51

○ 39

21. What is the sum?

$$64 + 9 = \boxed{}$$

○ 75   ○ 63

○ 73   ○ 55

22. What is the sum?

$$\begin{array}{r} 75 \\ + \ 15 \\ \hline \end{array}$$

○ 60   ○ 85

○ 80   ○ 90

Use the picture graph for Questions 23–24.

Favorite Color					
blue	☺	☺	☺		
green	☺	☺			
red	☺	☺	☺	☺	☺

Key: Each ☺ stands for 1 child.

23. How many children in all picked a favorite color?

○ 3   ○ 7

○ 5   ○ 10

24. 2 more children choose green. How many ☺ should be in the green row now?

○ 7   ○ 4

○ 5   ○ 3

GO ON

25. Ian made a tally chart of the flowers he planted.

Flowers Planted	
Flower	**Tally**
roses	IIII
daisies	IIII III
tulips	IIII

How many tulips did Ian plant?

○ 4 ○ 6
○ 5 ○ 8

26. Use the bar graph.

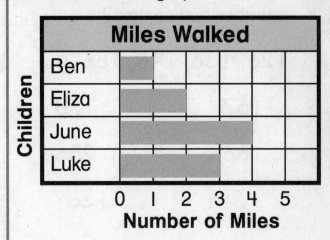

Who walked the **fewest** number of miles?

○ Ben ○ June
○ Eliza ○ Luke

27. Which number has the digit 4 in the hundreds place?

○ 42
○ 140
○ 453
○ 964

28. Which shows another way to write the number?

five hundred thirty-seven

○ 5 + 3 + 7
○ 50 + 37
○ 50 + 30 + 7
○ 500 + 30 + 7

GO ON

29. Look at the pattern. What number comes next?

126, 136, 146, 156, ▨

○ 157   ○ 178

○ 166   ○ 256

30. Which of the following is **true**?

○ 325 > 318

○ 390 = 309

○ 476 < 267

○ 510 > 723

---

31. What is the total value of the coins?

26¢   36¢   41¢   66¢
○   ○   ○   ○

---

32. Lara wants to buy a marker that costs one dollar. Which coins have a total value of one dollar?

○ 100 dimes

○ 100 pennies

○ 10 pennies

○ 10 nickels

GO ON ➡

33. Jason went on a morning run
at the time shown on the clock.
At what time did Jason go for his run?

10:45 a.m.	10:45 p.m.	9:55 a.m.	9:55 p.m.
○	○	○	○

---

34. Break apart the ones to subtract. What is the difference?

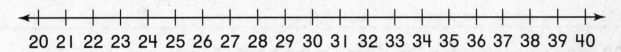

$$33 - 6 = \underline{\hspace{1cm}}$$

30	29	28	27
○	○	○	○

---

35. Rita had 37 pencils. She gave
away 14 pencils. Which number
sentence can be used to find
how many pencils Rita has now?

○ $23 - \boxed{} = 14$

○ $30 + \boxed{} = 37$

○ $37 - 14 = \boxed{}$

○ $37 + 14 = \boxed{}$

36. Steven picks 22 berries. He
picks 18 more berries. Then
he eats 13 berries. How many
berries does Steven have now?

○ 5

○ 27

○ 37

○ 40

GO ON ➡

37. What is the difference?

$$93$$
$$- 27$$

○ 76   ○ 66

○ 74   ○ 64

38. Which statement is **true?**

○ I centimeter is longer than I meter.

○ I meter is longer than I centimeter.

○ I meter is shorter than I centimeter.

○ I meter is the same as I centimeter.

39. Use a centimeter ruler. Which is the **best** choice for the length of this spoon?

○ 14 centimeters   ○ 10 centimeters

○ 12 centimeters   ○ 8 centimeters

40. Use a centimeter ruler. Measure the length of each object.

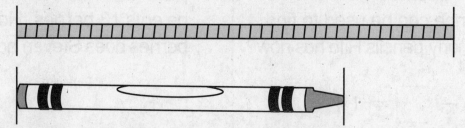

How much longer is the ribbon than the crayon?

○ 21 centimeters longer   ○ 9 centimeters longer

○ 12 centimeters longer   ○ 3 centimeters longer

Choose the correct answer.

1. Which shows a related subtraction fact?

$$9 + 5 = 14$$

○ $19 - 14 = 5$

○ $14 + 5 = 19$

○ $14 - 5 = 9$

○ $9 - 5 = 4$

2. There were 16 birds at the park. Then 9 birds flew away. Which number sentence shows how many birds are at the park now?

○ $16 + 9 = 25$

○ $16 - 9 = 7$

○ $9 - 7 = 2$

○ $2 + 7 = 9$

3. Fran picks 3 red flowers, 7 yellow flowers, and 3 pink flowers. How many flowers does Fran pick in all?

○ 6

○ 10

○ 12

○ 13

4. There are 429 students at the museum. There are 180 boys. How many girls are at the museum?

Hundreds	Tens	Ones
☐	☐	☐
4	2	9
− 1	8	0

○ 239   ○ 349

○ 249   ○ 369

5. What is the sum?

$$263 + 451$$

○ 724   ○ 624

○ 714   ○ 614

6. What is the difference?

$$507 - 368$$

○ 139   ○ 239

○ 149   ○ 241

7. Use an inch ruler. What is the length of the pencil to the nearest inch?

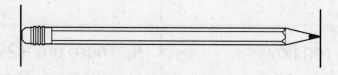

○ 5 inches   ○ 3 inches

○ 4 inches   ○ 2 inches

8. Use the line plot.
How many toy trucks are 4 inches long?

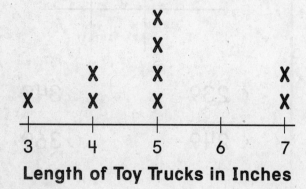

Length of Toy Trucks in Inches

○ 1

○ 2

○ 4

○ 5

GO ON

9. Which is the **best** estimate of the length of a real park bench?

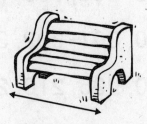

- ○ 1 foot
- ○ 6 feet
- ○ 15 feet
- ○ 20 feet

10. Frank wants to measure the length of a bus. Which is the **best** tool for Frank to use?

- ○ yardstick
- ○ counters
- ○ cup
- ○ pencil

11. Ms. Ikeda writes an even number on the board. Which could be the number that Ms. Ikeda writes?

- ○ 7
- ○ 11
- ○ 13
- ○ 14

12. What is the value of the underlined digit?

4<u>5</u>

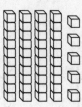

- ○ 50
- ○ 5
- ○ 40
- ○ 4

GO ON

13. Which shows another way to write the number?

32

○ twenty-three

○ 3 + 2

○ 3 tens 2 ones

○ 20 + 3

14. Which group of numbers shows counting by tens?

○ 400, 500, 600, 700

○ 300, 301, 302, 303

○ 200, 205, 210, 215

○ 100, 110, 120, 130

15. Which object is shaped like a cone?

16. Which names a shape with 6 sides and 6 vertices?

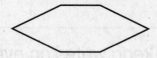

○ triangle

○ quadrilateral

○ pentagon

○ hexagon

GO ON ➤

17. Which of these shapes has **fewer** than 5 angles?

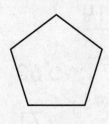

○

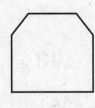

○

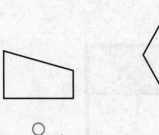

○

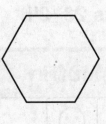

○

18. Which shows a third of the shape shaded?

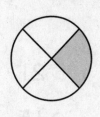

○

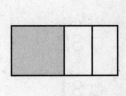

○

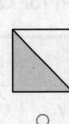

○

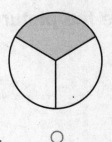

○

19. Which number will make this number sentence true?

■ + 8 = 5 + 7

○ 3

○ 4

○ 5

○ 6

20. What is the sum?

$$\begin{array}{r} 18 \\ 32 \\ + \ 12 \\ \hline \end{array}$$

○ 62

○ 52

○ 50

○ 44

GO ON ➤

21. What is the sum?

$$23 + 8 = \blacksquare$$

○ 32   ○ 21

○ 31   ○ 15

22. What is the sum?

$$57$$
$$+\ 14$$

○ 43   ○ 63

○ 61   ○ 71

Use the picture graph for Questions 23–24.

Favorite Muffin					
berry	☺	☺	☺		
corn	☺	☺	☺	☺	☺
pumpkin	☺				

Key: Each ☺ stands for 1 child.

23. How many children in all picked a favorite muffin?

○ 5   ○ 8

○ 6   ○ 9

24. 2 more children choose pumpkin. How many ☺ should be in the pumpkin row now?

○ 3   ○ 5

○ 4   ○ 7

GO ON

25. Julio made a tally chart of the vegetables he planted.

Vegetables Planted	
Vegetable	**Tally**
beans	ⅢⅠ I
carrots	ⅢⅠ
peas	ⅢⅠ II

How many peas did Julio plant?

○ 4   ○ 7

○ 6   ○ 10

26. Use the bar graph.

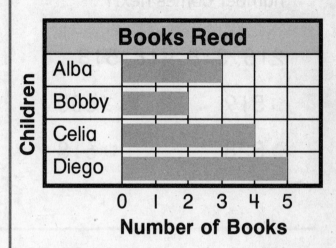

Who read the **most** books?

○ Alba   ○ Celia

○ Bobby   ○ Diego

27. Which number has the digit 8 in the tens place?

○ 18

○ 586

○ 298

○ 803

28. Which shows another way to write the number?

seven hundred thirteen

○ 7 + 13

○ 70 + 13

○ 70 + 10 + 3

○ 700 + 10 + 3

GO ON

29. Look at the pattern. What number comes next?

218, 318, 418, 518,

○ 519   ○ 600

○ 528   ○ 618

30. Which of the following is **true?**

○ 409 < 451

○ 623 < 517

○ 675 = 657

○ 730 > 874

---

31. What is the total value of the coins?

33¢   38¢   42¢   47¢
○   ○   ○   ○

---

32. Clara wants to buy a comb that costs one dollar. Which coins have a total value of one dollar?

○ 20 dimes

○ 20 nickels

○ 5 dimes

○ 5 nickels

GO ON

33. Jared ate lunch at the time shown on the clock. At what time did Jared eat lunch?

12:15 a.m.   12:15 p.m.   3:00 a.m.   3:00 p.m.
  ○   ○   ○   ○

---

34. Break apart the ones to subtract. What is the difference?

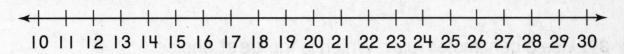

10 11 12 13 14 15 16 17 18 19 20 21 22 23 24 25 26 27 28 29 30

$$24 - 6 = \underline{\hspace{2cm}}$$

20   19   18   17
○   ○   ○   ○

---

35. Ana has 36 cups. She fills 12 cups with juice. Which number sentence can be used to find how many cups are empty?

○ $12 + \boxed{} = 30$

○ $24 - \boxed{} = 12$

○ $36 + 12 = \boxed{}$

○ $36 - 12 = \boxed{}$

36. Mark has 59 shells. He gives 21 shells to Ethan and 16 shells to Beth. How many shells does Mark have now?

○ 22

○ 37

○ 38

○ 43

GO ON ➡

37. What is the difference?

$$40$$
$$- \ 16$$

- ○ 24
- ○ 34
- ○ 36
- ○ 56

38. Which statement is **true?**

- ○ I meter is the same as I centimeter.
- ○ I meter is shorter than I centimeter.
- ○ I centimeter is longer than I meter.
- ○ I centimeter is shorter than I meter.

39. Use a centimeter ruler. Which is the **best** choice for the length of this marker?

- ○ 16 centimeters
- ○ 14 centimeters
- ○ 12 centimeters
- ○ 10 centimeters

40. Use a centimeter ruler. Measure the length of each object.

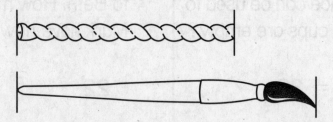

How much longer is the paintbrush than the string?

- ○ 16 centimeters longer
- ○ 10 centimeters longer
- ○ 8 centimeters longer
- ○ 2 centimeters longer

Choose the correct answer.

1. Which shows a related addition fact?

$$17 - 9 = 8$$

○ $17 + 9 = 26$

○ $9 - 8 = 1$

○ $8 + 9 = 17$

○ $25 - 8 = 17$

2. There are 7 big dogs and 6 small dogs. Which number sentence shows how many dogs there are in all?

○ $7 + 6 = 13$

○ $7 - 1 = 6$

○ $10 + 7 = 17$

○ $19 - 7 = 12$

3. Tess collects 2 green leaves, 8 red leaves, and 5 yellow leaves. How many leaves does Tess collect in all?

○ 7

○ 10

○ 13

○ 15

4. There are 545 seats at the theater. 362 seats are filled. How many seats are empty?

Hundreds	Tens	Ones
☐	☐	☐
5	4	5
− 3	6	2

○ 283   ○ 183

○ 223   ○ 123

GO ON

5. What is the sum?

$$
\begin{array}{r}
179 \\
+\ 515 \\
\hline
\end{array}
$$

○ 794   ○ 694

○ 784   ○ 684

6. What is the difference?

$$
\begin{array}{r}
803 \\
-\ 427 \\
\hline
\end{array}
$$

○ 486   ○ 386

○ 476   ○ 376

7. Use an inch ruler. What is the length of the paintbrush to the nearest inch?

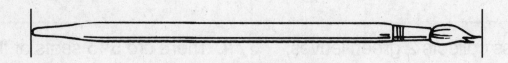

○ 4 inches   ○ 6 inches

○ 5 inches   ○ 7 inches

8. Use the line plot.
How many toy planes are 4 inches long?

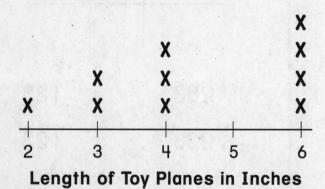

Length of Toy Planes in Inches

○ 2

○ 3

○ 4

○ 6

GO ON

9. Which is the **best** estimate of the length of an adult's shoe?

- ○ I foot
- ○ 3 feet
- ○ 5 feet
- ○ 9 feet

10. Eddie wants to measure the distance around a water bottle. Which is the **best** tool for Eddie to use?

- ○ cup
- ○ measuring tape
- ○ pencil
- ○ counters

11. Ms. Martinez writes an even number on the board. Which could be the number that Ms. Martinez writes?

- ○ 13
- ○ 11
- ○ 10
- ○ 9

12. What is the value of the underlined digit?

<u>6</u>2

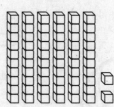

- ○ 2
- ○ 6
- ○ 20
- ○ 60

GO ON ➡

13. Which shows another way to write the number?

74

- ○ 4 tens 7 ones
- ○ forty-seven
- ○ 7 + 4
- ○ 70 + 4

14. Which group of numbers shows counting by hundreds?

- ○ 400, 405, 410, 415
- ○ 500, 510, 520, 530
- ○ 600, 700, 800, 900
- ○ 700, 701, 702, 703

15. Which object is shaped like a cube?

○

○

○

○

16. Which names a shape with 5 sides and 5 vertices?

- ○ triangle
- ○ quadrilateral
- ○ pentagon
- ○ hexagon

GO ON ➡

17. Which of these shapes has **more** than 5 sides?

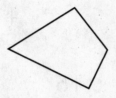

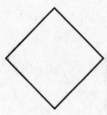

○   ○

18. Which shows a fourth of the shape shaded?

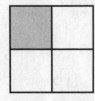   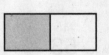

   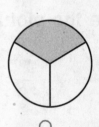

○   ○

---

19. Which number will make this number sentence true?

$$15 - \blacksquare = 17 - 9$$

○ 9

○ 7

○ 5

○ 4

20. What is the sum?

$$\begin{array}{r} 43 \\ 27 \\ + 13 \\ \hline \end{array}$$

○ 40

○ 70

○ 73

○ 83

GO ON

21. What is the sum?

$$47 + 6 = \blacksquare$$

○ 53   ○ 43

○ 52   ○ 41

22. What is the sum?

$$\begin{array}{r} 38 \\ + \ 23 \\ \hline \end{array}$$

○ 15   ○ 55

○ 51   ○ 61

Use the picture graph for Questions 23–24.

Favorite Meal					
breakfast	☺	☺			
lunch	☺	☺	☺		
dinner	☺	☺	☺	☺	☺

Key: Each ☺ stands for 1 child.

23. How many children in all picked a favorite meal?

○ 3   ○ 8

○ 5   ○ 10

24. 2 more children choose lunch. How many ☺ should be in the lunch row now?

○ 2   ○ 5

○ 4   ○ 7

GO ON

25. Mr. Campa made a tally chart of the trees he sold.

Trees Sold	
Tree	**Tally**
apple	卌 IIII
oak	III
pine	卌 I

How many pine trees did Mr. Campa sell?

○ 3   ○ 9

○ 6   ○ 10

26. Use the bar graph.

How We Get to School

Way

Bike
Bus
Car
Walk

0 1 2 3 4 5
Number of Children

How many children do **not** take the bus to school?

○ 6   ○ 2

○ 3   ○ 1

27. Which number has the digit 2 in the hundreds place?

○ 20

○ 742

○ 298

○ 25

28. Which shows another way to write the number?

four hundred twenty-three

○ 4 + 2 + 3

○ 40 + 23

○ 400 + 20 + 3

○ 400 + 20 + 30

GO ON

29. Look at the pattern. What number comes next?

351, 361, 371, 381, ▊

- ○ 382
- ○ 386
- ○ 391
- ○ 481

30. Which of the following is **true?**

- ○ 274 > 269
- ○ 285 = 280
- ○ 367 < 267
- ○ 508 > 941

31. What is the total value of the coins?

70¢   61¢   60¢   52¢

○   ○   ○   ○

32. Hugo wants to buy a bottle of juice that costs one dollar. Which coins have a total value of one dollar?

- ○ 10 quarters
- ○ 10 nickels
- ○ 4 quarters
- ○ 4 nickels

Name _____

33. Emily went to bed for the night at
the time shown on the clock.
At what time did Emily go to bed?

5:40 a.m.   5:40 p.m.   8:25 a.m.   8:25 p.m.
   ○   ○   ○   ○

---

34. Break apart the ones to subtract. What is the difference?

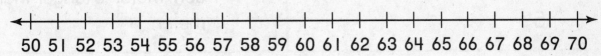

50 51 52 53 54 55 56 57 58 59 60 61 62 63 64 65 66 67 68 69 70

$$62 - 6 = \underline{\hspace{2cm}}$$

68   60   58   56
   ○   ○   ○   ○

---

35. Mia had 48 stickers. She
gave away 17 stickers. Which
number sentence can be used
to find how many stickers Mia
has now?

○ $40 + \boxed{} = 48$

○ $48 - 17 = \boxed{}$

○ $48 + 17 = \boxed{}$

○ $65 - \boxed{} = 48$

36. Jamal has a box with
35 crayons. He puts 22 more
crayons in the box. Then he
takes 14 crayons out of the
box. How many crayons are in
the box now?

○ 57

○ 53

○ 43

○ 8

GO ON ➡

37. What is the difference?

$$
\begin{array}{r}
81 \\
-\ 25 \\
\hline
\end{array}
$$

○ 66

○ 64

○ 56

○ 54

38. Which statement is **true?**

○ I meter is longer than
1 centimeter.

○ I meter is shorter than
1 centimeter.

○ I centimeter is the same
as 1 meter.

○ I centimeter is longer than
1 meter.

39. Use a centimeter ruler. Which is the **best** choice
for the length of this pencil?

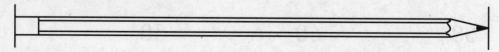

○ 15 centimeters

○ 13 centimeters

○ 11 centimeters

○ 9 centimeters

40. Use a centimeter ruler. Measure the length of each object.

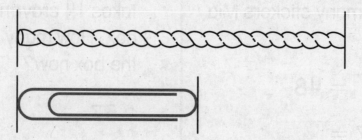

How much longer is the string than the paperclip?

○ 14 centimeters longer

○ 9 centimeters longer

○ 5 centimeters longer

○ 4 centimeters longer

1. Owen wants to measure the length of a chalkboard.

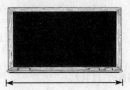

Circle the best choice of tool.

| tiles   inch ruler   yardstick |

Explain your choice of tool.

_____

_____

2. Meg has a ribbon that is 9 inches long. She has another ribbon that is 11 inches long. How many inches of ribbon does Meg have?

Draw a diagram. Write a number sentence using a ▓ for the missing number. Solve.

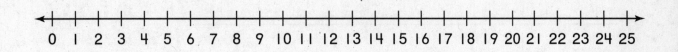

Meg has _____ inches of ribbon.

GO ON ➡

3. Use an inch ruler. What is the length of the string to the nearest inch?

Circle the number in the box to make the sentence true.

The string is
2
3
4
inches long.

4. Zach uses tiles to measure a straw. Each tile is 1 inch long. Zach says the straw is 4 inches long. Is he correct? Explain.

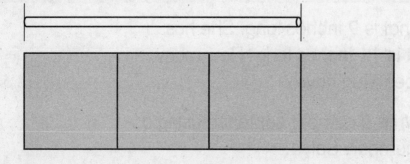

_____

_____

GO ON

5. Drew made a line plot to show the lengths of his toy boats.

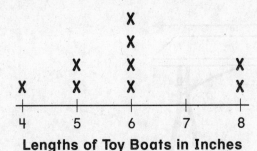

Lengths of Toy Boats in Inches

How many boats are shown in the line plot?

The line plot shows _____ toy boats.

How many boats are 5 inches long?

_____ boats

6. Use the words on the tiles to make the sentence true.

The boy is 40 _____ tall.

The car is 12 _____ long.

The driveway is 35 _____ long.

inches	feet

7. Use the 1-inch mark. Estimate the length of each piece of yarn.

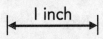
1 inch

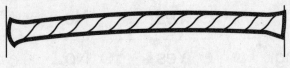
about _____ inches

about _____ inches

GO ON ➡

8. What is the best estimate for the length of the table top?

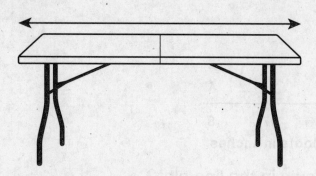

○ 2 yardsticks, or 2 yards

○ 6 yardsticks, or 6 yards

○ 10 yardsticks, or 10 yards

○ 12 yardsticks, or 12 yards

---

9. Estimate how many 12-inch rulers will be about the same length as a rug in your home.

Does the sentence describe the rug? Choose Yes or No.

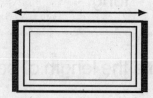

The rug is less than 1 foot long.	○ Yes	○ No
The rug is about 4 rulers long.	○ Yes	○ No
The rug is more than 20 feet long.	○ Yes	○ No
The rug is more than 1 ruler long.	○ Yes	○ No

STOP

1. Susan uses unit cubes to measure the length of the yarn. Circle the number in the box that makes the sentence true.

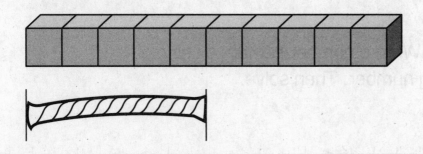

The yarn is about | 2 5 9 | centimeters long.

---

2. The paintbrush is about 7 centimeters long.
Gavin says the feather is about 8 centimeters long.
Ray says the feather is about 5 centimeters long.

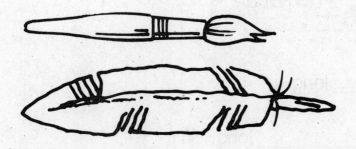

Which boy has the better estimate? Explain.

_____

_____

_____

GO ON ▶

3. Alberto uses 8 centimeters of wire for a science project. He uses another 15 centimeters of wire for another project. How many centimeters of wire does he use?

Draw a diagram. Write a number sentence using a ▨ for the missing number. Then solve.

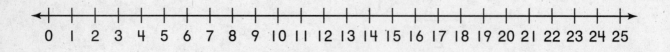

_____

Alberto uses _____ centimeters of wire.

_____

4. Write the word on the tile that makes the sentence true.

centimeters   meters

A pencil is 16 _____ long.

A swimming pool is 50 _____ long.

A bed is 2 _____ long.

A computer keyboard is 42 _____ long.

GO ON

5. Estimate the length of a real horse. Fill in the bubble next to all the sentences that are true.

○ The horse is less than 1 meter long.

○ The horse is less than 100 meters long.

○ The horse is more than 3 centimeters long.

○ The horse is about 6 centimeters long.

○ The horse is more than 100 centimeters long.

6. Measure the length of each object. Does the sentence describe the objects? Choose Yes or No.

_____ centimeters

_____ centimeters

The yarn is 3 centimeters longer than the crayon.	○ Yes	○ No
The crayon is 7 centimeters shorter than the yarn.	○ Yes	○ No
The total length of the yarn and the crayon is 17 centimeters.	○ Yes	○ No

GO ON ➡

7. Elizabeth has a piece of ribbon that is 25 centimeters long. She cuts off a piece of the ribbon to wrap a gift. Elizabeth's ribbon is now 7 centimeters long. How many centimeters of ribbon did Elizabeth use to wrap the gift?

Write a number sentence using a ■ for the unknown number. Then solve.

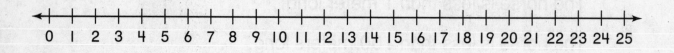

_____

Elizabeth used _____ centimeters of ribbon.

8. Measure the length of the rope to the nearest centimeter. Circle the number in the box that makes the sentence true.

The rope is about
12
13
15

centimeters long.

STOP

1. Nathan asked his friends to name their favorite vegetable. Use the data to make a tally chart.

peas—4 friends

carrots—9 friends

broccoli—1 friends

corn—5 friends

Favorite Vegetable	
Vegetable	**Tally**
peas	
carrots	
broccoli	
corn	

2. Does the sentence describe the data in the tally chart above? Choose Yes or No.

Broccoli is the least favorite vegetable.	○ Yes	○ No
More than 10 friends chose peas and carrots together.	○ Yes	○ No
More friends chose corn than carrots.	○ Yes	○ No

3. Nathan asks 7 more friends to choose their favorite vegetable. 6 friends choose peas and 1 friend chooses corn. Do more friends chose peas or carrots now? Explain.

_____

_____

_____

GO ON

4. Karina counted the number of sit-ups she did each day. Describe how the number of sit-ups changed from Monday to Thursday. Make a bar graph to solve the problem.

Monday—3 sit-ups   Wednesday—6 sit-ups

Tuesday—5 sit-ups   Thursday—8 sit-ups

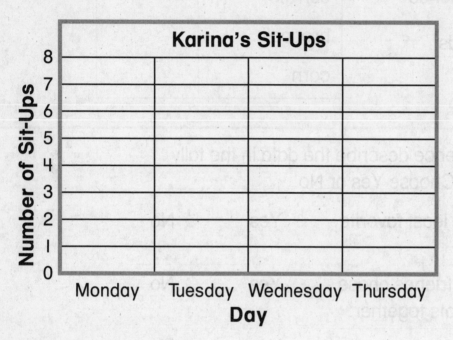

The number of sit-ups _____

_____

5. If Karina does 2 more sit-ups on Friday than she did on Thursday, how does the number of sit-ups change from Monday to Friday?

_____

_____

GO ON

6. Use the tally chart to complete the picture graph.
Draw a ☺ for each child.

Favorite School Subject	
math	IIII
reading	III
science	II
art	III

Favorite School Subject				
math				
reading				
science				
art				

Key: Each ☺ stands for I child.

7. How many children chose art?

_____ children

8. How many more children chose math than science?

_____ more children

9. Name two subjects that were chosen by a total of 6 children.

_____

GO ON ▶

10. Eric asked some friends to name their favorite sandwich. Use the data to complete the bar graph.

4 friends chose ham.

6 friends chose turkey.

I friend chose cheese.

3 friends chose jelly.

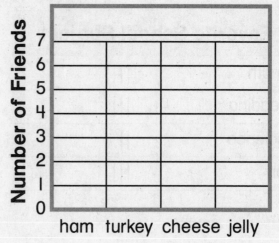

Number of Friends

ham turkey cheese jelly

_____

11. Fill in the bubble next to all the sentences that describe the data in the bar graph above.

○ 6 friends chose ham.

○ Turkey was chosen by the most friends.

○ 7 friends chose cheese and jelly together.

○ 5 more friends chose turkey than cheese.

12. Did more friends choose cheese and jelly together than ham? Explain.

_____

_____

13. How many friends chose a sandwich other than turkey?

_____ friends

1. Match the shapes.

2. Do the sentences describe a rectangular prism? Choose Yes or No.

A rectangular prism has 6 faces.	○ Yes	○ No
Each face of a rectangular prism is a square.	○ Yes	○ No
A rectangular prism has 16 vertices.	○ Yes	○ No
A rectangular prism has 12 edges.	○ Yes	○ No

Rewrite each sentence that is not true to make it a true sentence.

_____

_____

GO ON ➡

3. Draw lines to show fourths.

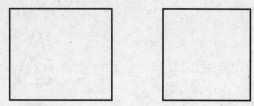

Explain how you know that the parts are fourths.

_____

_____

4. Hector makes two sandwiches that are the same
size. He cuts each sandwich into thirds. What are
two different ways he can cut the sandwiches?
Draw to show your answer.

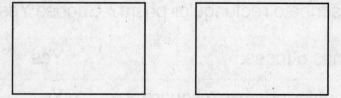

5. Draw to show halves, thirds, and fourths. Color a half of,
a third of, and a fourth of the shape.

 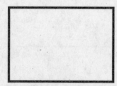

halves   **thirds**   **fourths**

GO ON

6. Grace wants to cover the rectangle with gray tiles. Explain how you would estimate the number of gray tiles she would need to cover the rectangle.

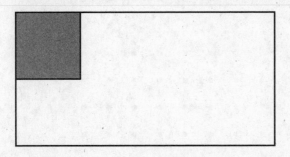

_____

_____

7. Alex built this rectangular prism. Circle the number of unit cubes Alex used.

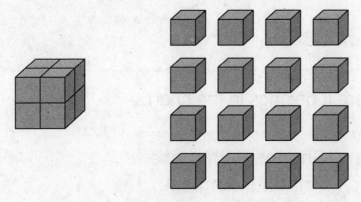

8. Paul makes a hexagon and a triangle with straws. He uses one straw for each side of a shape. How many straws does Paul need?

_____ straws

GO ON

9. Mason drew 2 two-dimensional shapes that had 8 angles in all. Draw the shapes Mason could have drawn.

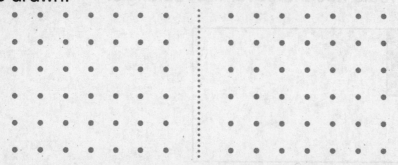

10. Fill in the bubble next to the shapes that show thirds.

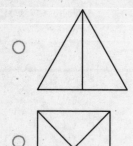

○

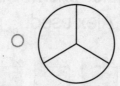

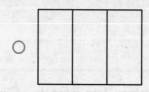

○

○

○

11. Draw each shape where it belongs in the chart.

Shapes with fewer than 5 angles	Shapes with more than 4 Angles

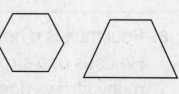

Basketball Games

It is Basketball Day at the gym.
First, the Green Team and the Blue Team
play a game.
The Green Team scores an even number
of points.
The Blue Team scores an odd number of points.
Each team's score is a 2-digit number.

1. Write a number of points that each team
could score.

Green Team _____   Blue Team _____

2. Look at the Green Team's score. What is the value
of the ones digit?

_____

3. Look at the Blue Team's score. What is the value of
the tens digit? Explain how you know.

_____

_____

_____

Next, the Red Team plays the Orange Team.
The Red Team scores 35 points.
The Orange Team scores more points
than the Red Team.
Jen writes the Red Team's score
3 different ways:

$10 + 25$ $20 + 15$ **3 tens 5 ones**

4. Write a number that could be the Orange Team's score. Then write the Orange Team's score 3 different ways.

5. There were 43 people at the first game. The number of people went up by 10 each game for the next 3 games. Count the number of people by tens.

43, _____, _____, _____

6. A local school has a much bigger gym and had 220 people at their first game. The number of people went up by 100 each game for the next 3 games. Count the number of people by hundreds.

220, _____, _____, _____

The Apartment Building

**There is a big apartment building near the park.
Each apartment has a 3-digit number.
Jose's apartment number has the digit 9 in the
ones place and the digit 1 in the hundreds place.**

1. Write a number that could be Jose's apartment
number.

_____

2. Erik lives in another apartment in the same building.
The number of his apartment is 100 more than the
number of Jose's apartment. What could Erik's
apartment number be?

_____

3. Marta lives in apartment 450. Write a number
sentence that uses the symbols >, <, or = to
compare Marta's apartment number and Erik's
apartment number.

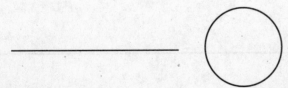

_____   _____

4. Kim lives in apartment number 513. She uses blocks to show her apartment number. Draw a quick picture to show Kim's apartment number.

5. Chang's apartment number is 10 more than Kim's apartment number. What is Chang's apartment number? What are two other ways to write this number?

_____   _____

_____

6. Anya uses groups of 10 buttons to show her apartment number. She uses 17 groups of buttons with 2 buttons left over. What is her apartment number?

_____

At the Zoo

Martin's class visits the zoo.

1. There are some brown bears and some white bears.
   There are 12 bears in all.
   How many brown and white bears could there be?
   Write a number sentence to show your answer.

   _____ brown bears   _____ white bears

   _____

2. Martin sees 3 rows of cages in the bird house.
   There are 3 cages in each row.
   How many cages are in the bird house?

   Complete the number sentence to solve.

   _____ + _____ + _____ = _____

   There are ____ cages.

There are 13 monkeys at the monkey house.
8 of the monkeys are outside.
The rest of the monkeys are inside.

3. How many monkeys are inside? Draw or write
   to show how you found your answer.

_____ monkeys inside

4. How many more monkeys are outside than inside?
   Draw or write to show how you found your answer.

_____ more monkeys

5. Martin counts 7 baby seals and 8 adult seals.
   Find the sum. Then write the related addition fact.

$7 + 8 =$ _____   _____ $+$ _____ $=$ _____

Brick Towers

Some friends are building towers with bricks.
Some of the bricks are big. The rest are small.

Tower A uses 47 bricks.
Tower B uses 52 bricks.
Tower C uses 45 bricks.

1. Kumari's favorite tower uses 35 big bricks and
   17 small bricks.

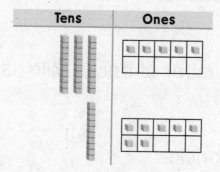

Which tower is Kumari's favorite?

Tower _____

2. How many total bricks are in Tower A and Tower C?

_____

3. Which two towers use a total of 99 bricks?

Tower _____ and Tower _____

la made these models to show how many bricks
she used to make Towers D and E.

Tower D

Tens	Ones

Tower E

Tens	Ones

4. How many bricks did Mila use to build Tower D?

_____ bricks

5. What is the total number of bricks Mila used to make Towers D and E?

_____ bricks

6. You are asked to build a tower that has 62 bricks in total. Use some big bricks and some small bricks. How many big bricks and how many small bricks will you use?

_____ big bricks   _____ small bricks

The Farmers Market

Maggie goes to the farmers market with her family. There are 32 farmers selling food at the market.

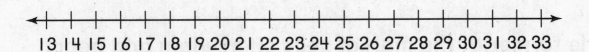

13 14 15 16 17 18 19 20 21 22 23 24 25 26 27 28 29 30 31 32 33

1. There are 13 farmers who sell fruit.
How many farmers do NOT sell fruit?

_____ farmers

2. Of the 32 farmers at the market, there are 5 farmers who do NOT sell vegetables. How many farmers sell vegetables?

_____ farmers

3. There are 47 apples in a big basket at the market.
There are 24 apples in a small basket.

How many more apples are in the big basket than in the small basket?

Write a number sentence with a ▢ for the missing number. Then solve the problem.

_____   _____ more apples

4. One farmer at the market is selling juice. He has
a stack of 11 cups and a stack of 18 cups.

He needs 35 cups in all.
How many more cups does he need?

_____ cups

**One farmer at the market sells cherry jam and peach
jam.**

She sells 26 jars of jam in all.
She sells 17 jars of cherry jam.

5. How many jars of peach jam does the farmer sell?
Draw or write to show how you found your answer.

_____ jars

6. How many more jars of cherry jam than peach jam
does the farmer sell?

Draw or write to show how you found your answer.

_____ more jars

On the Subway

Carlos is on a subway train. There are 382 people on his train. Julia is on another subway train. There are 144 people on her train.

1. How many people in all are on the two trains?

_____ people

2. How many more people are on Carlos's train than on Julia's train?

_____ people

3. Carlos's train stops at a big station, and 240 people get off. Then at least 5 new people get on. Whose train has more people now—Carlos's or Julia's? Explain your answer.

_____

_____

_____

_____

This is how many people are waiting for trains at these stations.

Morris Park	York Street	Queens Plaza
135	358	163

4. Ella adds two of these numbers. She does NOT need to regroup. Which numbers does she add?

_____ and _____

5. How many more people are waiting at York Street than are waiting at Queens Plaza? Use quick pictures to show the numbers before and then after you regroup.

There are _____ more people waiting at York Street.

The Mall

1. The clock shows when the mall opens. Write the time.

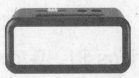

2. Lon plans to go to the mall at a time between 9:15 a.m. and 1:15 p.m. Draw hands on the clock to show when Lon might go to the mall. Then write the time.

3. The mall closes at 8:00. Is this an a.m. time or a p.m. time? How do you know?

_____

_____

_____

4. Yani buys a toy at the mall. He spends 3 dimes and 3 nickels. Show this amount using a different group of coins. Draw and label the coins.

5. Taylor brings $1.40 to spend at the mall. Draw a quick picture to show the bills and coins she might have.

6. You are at the mall. You can buy one thing.

| pencil 40¢ | | eraser 35¢ | | marker 50¢ |

Circle what you will buy.
Then show that amount in 2 different ways.
Draw and label the coins.

Art Class

In art class, some children are using ribbons.

1. Cindy is measuring some pieces of ribbon for a banner. The list shows the lengths of the pieces. Use the data in the list to complete the line plot.

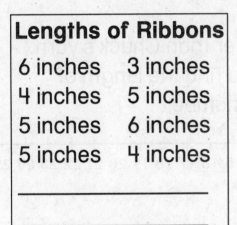

Lengths of Ribbons

6 inches	3 inches
4 inches	5 inches
5 inches	6 inches
5 inches	4 inches
_____	
_____	

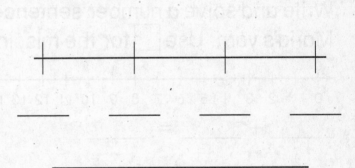

2. There are 2 pieces left to measure. Measure the ribbons and record the lengths in the list and on the line plot.

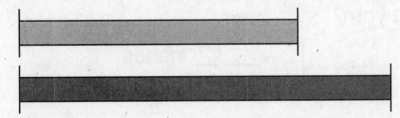

3. What tool did you select to measure the ribbon?

_____

Explain why you selected that tool.

_____

_____

measuring tape
inch ruler
yardstick

Some of the children are using beads and yarn. Each bead is one inch long.

4. Chuck makes a bead bracelet. He uses the yarn below. About how long is Chuck's piece of yarn?

about _____ inches

5. Maria's piece of yarn is 9 inches longer than Chuck's yarn. Write and solve a number sentence to find the length of Maria's yarn. Use ☐ for the missing number.

_____ + _____ = _____

Maria's yarn is _____ inches long.

6. Use an inch ruler. Measure the length to the nearest inch. How long is the yarn?

 _____ inches

7. Tyrone has a piece of yarn that is 3 feet long. He measures it again to find the number of inches. Will the number of feet or the number of inches be greater? Explain your answer.

_____

_____

Making a Birdhouse

Use a centimeter ruler for Exercises 1 and 2.

1. Karl and Nisha are making a birdhouse. They are going to use nails that look like this.

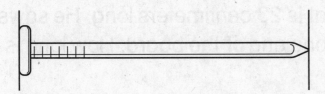

What is the length of the nail to the nearest centimeter?

_____ centimeters

2. Karl and Nisha will use string to hang their birdhouse from a tree. About how much longer is the top piece of string than the bottom piece?

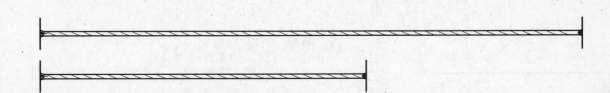

_____ − _____ = _____

_____ centimeters longer

3. Nisha uses a pencil to mark the wood for cutting. The paper clip is about 3 centimeters long. Circle the best estimate for the length of the pencil.

5 centimeters

9 centimeters

20 centimeters

4. Karl has a board that is 23 centimeters long. He saws 15 centimeters off one end of the board. How long is the board now?

The board is _____ centimeters long now.

5. When the birdhouse is finished, Nisha and Karl want to measure its height. Should they measure the height of the birdhouse with a meter stick or a centimeter ruler?

_____

Explain your answer.

_____

_____

_____

Our Favorites

The children in Mr. Scott's class are collecting data.
Omar asks 14 children which color is their favorite.
He displays the data on a picture graph.

Some children choose blue. More children choose yellow than red.

One child chooses green. Three children choose red.

1. Complete the graph to show what Omar's graph
   could look like. Draw a ☺ for each child.

Favorite Color								

Key: Each ☺ stands for 1 child.

2. How many children in all choose blue and yellow?

_____ children

How do you know your answer is correct?

_____

_____

_____

Marci asks some children which pet is their favorite.
She makes a tally chart to show the data.

Favorite Pet	
Pet	**Tally**
Cat	IIII IIII I
Rabbit	IIII
Dog	IIII III

3. How many children choose dog?

_____ children

4. How many more children choose cat than rabbit?

_____ more children

5. Sanjay asks 12 children which sport is their favorite.
He makes a bar graph to show the data. There are
4 children who choose baseball. Complete the
graph to show what it could look like.

Favorite Sport										
baseball										
soccer										
running										
swimming										

Sports

0 1 2 3 4 5 6 7 8 9 10
Number of Children

Windows in the City

Kai and Alicia are looking at the windows in their city.
The windows are in many different shapes.

1. Kai sees a window that has a shape he really likes.
   The window has all straight sides. It has more than
   4 angles and fewer than 7 angles.

   Draw a shape that the window could be.

2. Alicia sees a window in this shape.

   What is the name of this shape? _____
   How many sides does it have? _____ sides
   How many vertices does it have?
   _____ vertices

3. Kai sees a window in the shape of a circle.
The circle is divided into fourths.
Draw to show the window that Kai sees.

4. Alicia sees a window in the shape of a rectangle.
The window is divided into 3 equal parts.
Each part is called a _____.
Draw lines to show 2 ways a rectangle can be
divided into 3 equal parts.

5. Kai also sees a window in the shape of a rectangle.
What is the total number of same-size square glass
tiles that could cover the window?

Total: _____ glass tiles

6. Alicia sees 3 windows. Each window is in the shape
of a quadrilateral. How many sides are there in all?

_____ sides

Explain how you know. _____

_____

_____

Two Schools

Jefferson School has students in 1st grade up to 5th grade.

1. The number of children in 1st grade has 3 digits.
   The digits in the number are 2, 3, and 8.
   The digit 8 means 80 in this number.
   Write a number that could be the number of children in 1st grade.

   _____

2. Write a number that is 10 less than the number of children you chose for 1st grade.

   _____

3. Write a number sentence that uses >, <, or =
   to compare your answers from questions 1 and 2.

   _____ ◯ _____

4. Donell uses these blocks to show the number of students in 3rd grade.

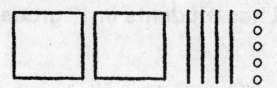

How many students are in 3rd grade?

_____ students

5. There are 100 more students in 4th grade than in 5th grade. Grade 5 has 176 students. Draw a quick picture to show how many students are in 4th grade.

6. Write a number sentence that uses >, <, or = to compare the number of students in 4th grade with the number of students in 3rd grade.

_____ ◯ _____

Name _____

Yasmeen goes to Lincoln School. She counts the number of 2nd grade students who go there. The number in the circle is the total number of 2nd grade students at Lincoln School.

7. Fill in the missing numbers. Count by tens.

220, 230, _____, _____, _____, _____, _____

8. Yasmeen uses tens blocks to show the number of 2nd grade students. How many tens blocks will she need?

She will need _____ blocks.

9. Suppose Yasmeen's school has 210 students in 3rd grade. How would you figure out a number that is 10 more than that? Write your answer. Explain how you know.

_____

_____

_____

_____

The number of students at Jefferson School is even.
The number has three digits.
The digit in the tens place is 4.

10. Write three numbers that could be how many students there are at Jefferson School.

_____   _____   _____

Explain how you know your answers are correct.

_____

_____

_____

11. Choose one of the numbers that you just wrote. Write it three different ways.

12. Write a 3-digit number that could NOT be the number of students at Jefferson School.

There could NOT be _____ students.

The Reading Challenge

Some children did a reading challenge.
They recorded how many books they read.

1. Miguel read 7 books. Mia read the same number
   of books as Miguel. Write and solve the number
   sentence to show how many books Miguel and
   Mia read in all.

   _____ + _____ = _____

2. Abdul read 8 books. Jose read 11 books.
   How many more books did Jose read than Abdul?

   _____ books

3. Estela read 23 books last month. She put the
   books onto three shelves. Each shelf has a
   different number of books.

   Write a number sentence to show how many
   books might be on each shelf.

   _____ + _____ + _____ = _____

**Franco read 22 books. Tia read 15 books.
Ali read more books than Tia but fewer than Franco.**

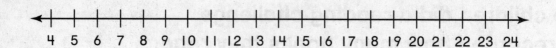

4. How many more books did Franco read than Tia?
   Use the number line to solve.

   _____ books

5. How many books could the 3 children have read in all?
   Write a number sentence.

   _____ + _____ + _____ = _____

   Explain your answer.

   _____

   _____

   _____

6. Erica read 31 books. Her friend Molly read 17 books.
Draw a quick picture to show how many books
Erica and Molly read in all.

They read _____ books in all.

7. Serena read a book that is 38 pages long. Ming read
a book that is 26 pages long. Rohan read a book
that is 31 pages long.

Ming finds how many pages he and Rohan read in all.
How many more pages did they read than Serena?

They read _____ more pages than Serena.

Explain how you know your answer is correct.

_____

_____

_____

_____

This tells how many books were read by all the children in 3 different classes.

Mr. Dorn's class	Ms. Lopez's class	Ms. Chen's class
319 books	185 books	241 books

8. How many books did the 3 classes read in all?

    _____ books

9. How many more books did Mr. Dorn's class read than Ms. Lopez's class?

    _____ books

10. The library has a shelf of storybooks. There are 473 new books on the shelf. The children at the school have already read 205 of these books. How many of the books have they NOT read yet?

    _____ books

The Museum Store

1. The museum store opens at 10:00 a.m.
   Eva gets to the store before 11:30 a.m.
   Draw hands on the clock to show when
   Eva might get to the store. Then write the time.

2. The clock shows when the store closes.
   Write the time.

   Is this an a.m. time or a p.m. time? Explain how you know.

   _____

   _____

   _____

3. Jin buys a bookmark.
She uses these coins to pay for the bookmark.
How much does she pay?

_____ ¢

4. Jin also buys a pencil.
The pencil costs more than the bookmark.
The pencil costs less than one dollar.

How much could the pencil cost?

The pencil could cost _____ ¢
Draw and label coins to show one way to make
this amount.

5. Jin compares the lengths of her crayon and her
pencil. The pencil is about 12 centimeters long.
What is a good estimate for the length of the
crayon?

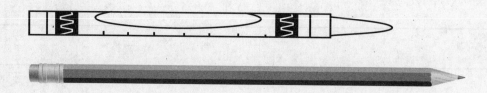

The crayon is about _____ centimeters long.

The picture graph shows how many toy trucks of each color are in the store.

Colors of Trucks									
red	☺	☺	☺						
blue	☺	☺	☺	☺	☺				
black	☺	☺	☺	☺					
white	☺	☺	☺						

Key: Each ☺ stands for 1 truck.

6. How many black trucks are there? ____

7. Write color names to complete the sentence.

The number of _____ trucks is equal

to the number of _____ trucks.

8. The clerk sold 20 stuffed animals on Wednesday. He sold bears, lions, foxes, and turtles. Three of the animals were bears. Make a bar graph to show the stuffed animals. Draw what the graph might look like.

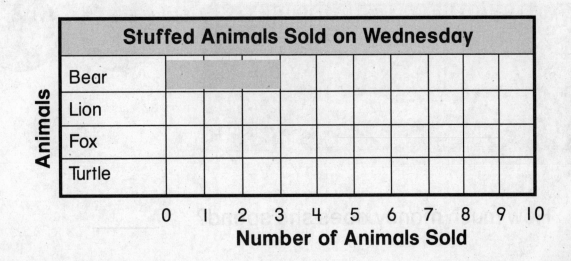

Stuffed Animals Sold on Wednesday

Animals: Bear, Lion, Fox, Turtle

Number of Animals Sold: 0 1 2 3 4 5 6 7 8 9 10

9. Grace buys a black pen at the store.

Use an inch ruler. Measure the length of the pen to the nearest inch.

The pen is about _____ inches long.

10. Grace also buys two banners for her room. The first is 33 inches long. The second banner is 19 inches long. How much longer is the first banner than the second banner?

_____ – _____ = _____

_____ inches longer

11. Grace uses this money to pay for her items.

How much money does she spend? _____

The Community Garden

The children in Ms. Rosa's class are working in a community garden.
Each child works in a different patch of the garden.
Each patch has a different shape.

1. Raina's patch of the garden has the shape of a quadrilateral.
   How many angles are in her shape?

   _____ angles

2. Conor's patch of the garden is a shape that has 3 sides and 3 angles. Circle the word that names Conor's shape.

   square   hexagon   triangle

3. Lana's patch of the garden is in the shape of a square. She uses 2 lines to divide the square into equal parts. Draw to show how she can do it.

   The square has _____ equal parts.
   Each part is a _____.

4. Kolten finds 3 shapes in the garden.
He finds a square, a hexagon, and one other shape
with fewer than 7 sides.
Draw Kolten's shapes.
Next, write how many sides his shapes have in all.

_____ sides in all

5. DeShawn's garden patch is in this shape.

How many sides and how many vertices does
DeShawn's shape have?

_____ sides   _____ vertices

6. Hiro's patch of the garden is in the shape of a circle.
Draw to show how Hiro can divide the circle into
3 equal parts.

What are the 3 equal parts of the
circle called? _____

Explain how you know.

_____

_____

7. Ms. Rosa keeps the gardening tools in a box that
has this shape.

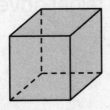

What is the name of this shape? _____
How many faces does it have? _____
How many vertices does it have? _____
How many edges does it have? _____

8. Jill's patch of the garden is in the shape of a rectangle. She wants to cover the rectangle with same-size squares of grass. What is the total number of same-size squares she will need to cover the rectangle?

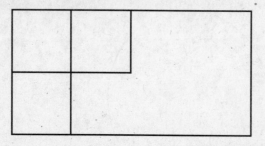

Jill will need a total of _____ squares.

9. Delta has a garden patch in the shape of a circle. She wants to divide her shape into halves. How many halves will she be able to make?

_____ halves

10. Mario is making signs for the garden.
He cuts 2 shapes out of cardboard.
He counts the angles of the two shapes.
The shapes have 9 angles in all.
Draw the two shapes Mario might have made.

Choose the correct answer.

1. Find the nearest ten for each number.
   Which shows the best estimate of 58 − 41?

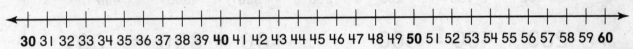

30 31 32 33 34 35 36 37 38 39 **40** 41 42 43 44 45 46 47 48 49 **50** 51 52 53 54 55 56 57 58 59 **60**

○ 60 − 50 = 10   ○ 60 − 30 = 30

○ 60 − 40 = 20   ○ 70 − 30 = 40

2. What the missing sum in the
   addition table?

○ 6

○ 7

○ 8

○ 9

+	0	1	2	3	4	5
0	0	1	2	3	4	5
1	1	2	3	4	5	6
2	2	3	4	5	6	7
3	3	4	5	6	7	8
4	4	5	6		8	9
5	5	6	7	8	9	10

3. Which shows the numbers in
   order from **least** to **greatest**?

465
378
460

○ 465 < 378 < 460

○ 378 < 465 < 460

○ 378 < 460 < 465

○ 460 < 465 < 378

4. There are 4 baskets. Hana
   puts 5 apples in each basket.

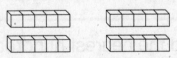

How many apples does she put
in the baskets?

○ 5   ○ 15

○ 9   ○ 20

GO ON →

5. Find the nearest hundred for each number.
   Which shows the best estimate of $130 + 370$?

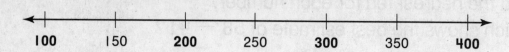

- ○ $200 + 400 = 600$
- ○ $100 + 300 = 400$
- ○ $100 + 400 = 500$
- ○ $100 + 200 = 300$

6. Caleb makes 5 towers. Each tower has 10 blocks.

How many blocks does he use?

- ○ 70
- ○ 60
- ○ 50
- ○ 10

7. What is the missing sum in the
   addition table?

+	0	1	2	3	4	5
0	0	1	2	3	4	5
1	1	2	3	4	5	6
2	2	3	4	5	6	7
3	3	4	5	6	7	8
4	4		6	7	8	9

- ○ 3
- ○ 5
- ○ 4
- ○ 6

8. Find the nearest hundred for each number.
   Which shows the best estimate of $829 - 632$?

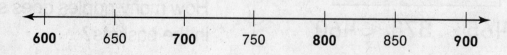

- ○ $900 - 500 = 400$
- ○ $800 - 600 = 200$
- ○ $800 - 500 = 300$
- ○ $800 - 700 = 100$

GO ON ➡

9. Mr. Roper puts 2 fish in each bowl. There are 5 bowls.

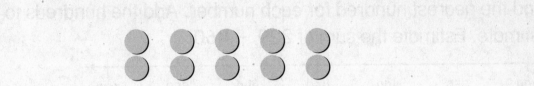

How many fish does Mr. Roper put in the bowls?

○ 2   ○ 7   ○ 10   ○ 12

---

10. Find the nearest ten for each number.
Which shows the best estimate of $31 + 27$?

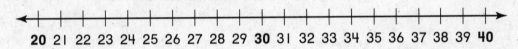

20 21 22 23 24 25 26 27 28 29 **30** 31 32 33 34 35 36 37 38 39 **40**

○ $30 + 20 = 50$ ○ $40 + 30 = 70$

○ $30 + 30 = 60$ ○ $40 + 40 = 80$

---

11. Aiden has 6 cheese slices. He puts the same number of cheese slices on each of 2 sandwiches.

How many cheese slices are on each sandwich?

○ 1   ○ 3

○ 2   ○ 4

12. There are 10 cubes in each box. There are 3 boxes of cubes.

How many cubes are there altogether?

○ 30   ○ 13

○ 20   ○ 10

GO ON ➤

Write the correct answer.

13. Find the nearest hundred for each number. Add the hundreds to estimate. Estimate the sum of $329 + 460$.

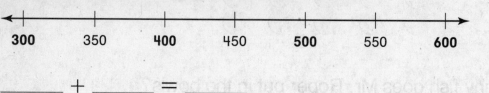

300 350 **400** 450 **500** 550 **600**

_____ + _____ = _____

An estimate of the sum is _____.

---

14. Amanda puts 2 stamps on each card.
How many stamps does she put on 6 cards?

_____ stamps

---

15. Write the numbers in order from **least** to **greatest**.

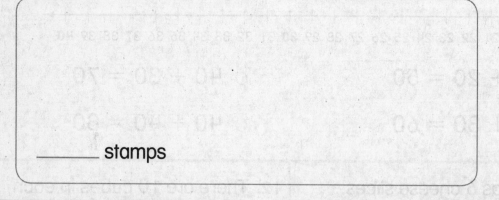

156
299
253

_____ < _____ < _____

16. Brad puts 2 tomatoes in each salad. There are 4 salads.

How many tomatoes does he use?

_____ tomatoes

GO ON

17. Connor gives 15 stickers to friends. He gives 3 stickers to each friend.

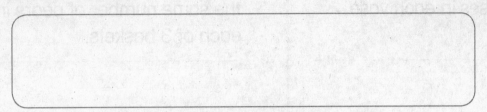

How many friends get stickers?

_____ friends

---

18. Find the nearest ten for each number. Add the tens to estimate. Estimate the sum of 34 + 48.

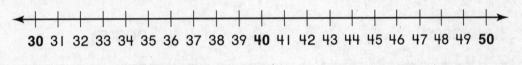

_____ + _____ = _____

An estimate of the sum is _____.

---

19. Sophia uses 10 blocks to build each tower. How many towers can she build with 40 blocks?

_____ towers

---

20. Find the nearest hundred for each number. Subtract the hundreds to estimate. Estimate the difference of 825 − 675.

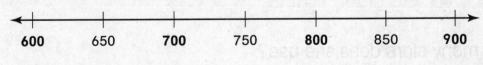

_____ − _____ = _____

An estimate of the difference is _____.

GO ON ➡

21. Mrs. Allen has 12 roses. She puts 3 roses in each vase.

How many vases can she fill?

_____ vases

22. Avery has 15 pears. She puts the same number of pears in each of 3 baskets.

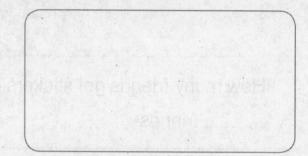

How many pears are in each basket?

_____ pears

23. Find the nearest ten for each number. Subtract the tens to estimate. Estimate the difference of 48 − 32.

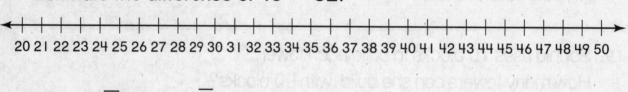

_____ − _____ = _____

An estimate of the difference is _____.

24. Hailey puts 5 stars on each bookmark. She makes 6 bookmarks.

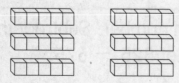

How many stars does she use?

_____ stars

STOP

Choose the correct answer.

1. The clock shows when the bus arrives. What time is **1 hour after** the time shown?

- ○ 11:00
- ○ 10:00
- ○ 9:00
- ○ 8:00

2. Cole uses the scoop and rice to fill the glass.

About how many scoops of rice does the glass hold?

- ○ 5 scoops
- ○ 10 scoops
- ○ 15 scoops
- ○ 20 scoops

3. Look at the gray part of the strip.

Which is the correct label?

- ○ 1 third
- ○ 2 thirds
- ○ 1 sixth
- ○ 2 sixths

4. David's soccer game begins at 3:00 P.M. It ends at 5:00 P.M. How long is the game?

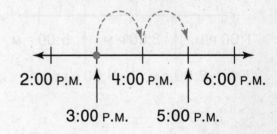

- ○ 4 hours
- ○ 3 hours
- ○ 2 hours
- ○ 1 hour

GO ON ▶

5. The clock shows when the game begins.

Justin gets to the game **1 hour before** the game begins. What time does Justin get to the game?

○ 11:00   ○ 12:00

○ 11:30   ○ 2:00

6. Use the line plot to solve the problem.

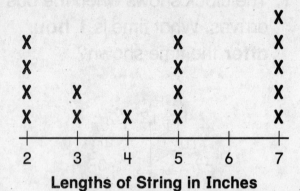

Lengths of String in Inches

What is the length of the longest string?

○ 3 inches   ○ 7 inches

○ 4 inches   ○ 8 inches

7. Brooke gets to the library at 2:00 P.M. She leaves at 4:00 P.M. How long does she stay at the library?

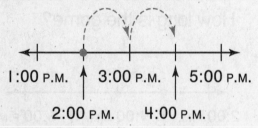

1:00 P.M.   3:00 P.M.   5:00 P.M.

   2:00 P.M.   4:00 P.M.

○ 1 hour

○ 2 hours

○ 3 hours

○ 4 hours

8. Levi gets on the train at 8:10 A.M. He gets off the train at 8:45 A.M. How long does he ride the train?

○ 55 minutes

○ 45 minutes

○ 35 minutes

○ 30 minutes

GO ON ➡

9. Look at the gray part of the strip.

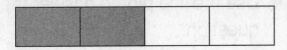

Which is the correct label?

○ I eighth

○ 2 fourths

○ I fourth

○ 2 eighths

10. Which is true?

half	half

fourth	fourth	fourth	fourth

○ I half > I fourth

○ I half < I fourth

○ I fourth = I half

○ I half < I fourth

11. Ms. Chapman uses the scoop to fill the bowl with rice.

About how many scoops of rice does the bowl hold?

○ I scoop

○ 3 scoops

○ 8 scoops

○ 9 scoops

12. Which is true?

half	half

sixth	sixth	sixth	sixth	sixth	sixth

○ I half > 4 sixths

○ I half < 4 sixths

○ 4 sixths < I half

○ I half = 4 sixths

GO ON

Write the correct answer.

13. The movie begins at 3:00 P.M. It is over at 6:00 P.M. How long is the movie?

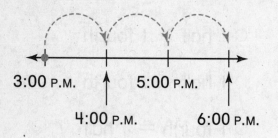

3:00 P.M.   5:00 P.M.

4:00 P.M.   6:00 P.M.

_____ hours

14. Use the line plot to answer the question.

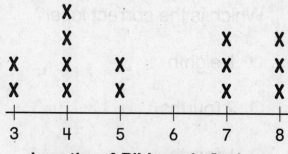

Lengths of Ribbons in Inches

How many ribbons are 3 inches long?

_____ ribbons

15. Look at the gray part of the strip.

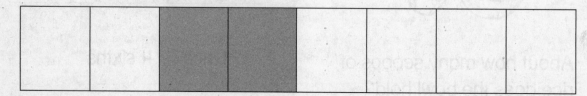

Which label is correct? Circle it.

2 fourths   2 eighths   4 eighths

16. Play practice begins at 3:15 P.M. Practice is over at 3:45 P.M. How long is play practice?

_____ minutes

17. Look at the gray part of the strip.

Which label is correct? Circle it.

1 third

2 thirds

2 sixths

18. Write >, <, or = to compare the fractions.

third	third	third

sixth	sixth	sixth	sixth	sixth	sixth

1 third ◯ 2 sixths

19. Use the line plot to solve the problem.

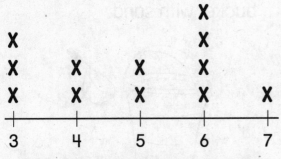

Lengths of Pencils in Inches

How long are the shortest pencils?

_____ inches

20. Look at the gray part of the strip.

Which label is correct? Circle it.

3 thirds

3 sixths

4 sixths

GO ON

21. Thomas gets to school **1 hour after** the time shown on the clock. What time does Thomas get to school?

_____

22. Look at the gray part of the strip.

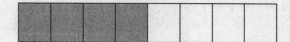

Which label is correct? Circle it.

3 fourths

4 fourths

4 eighths

23. Lunch begins at 12:10 P.M. It ends at 12:50 P.M. How long is lunch?

_____ minutes

24. Mai uses the scoop to fill the bucket with sand.

About how many scoops of sand does the bucket hold?

Circle the best estimate.

about 2 scoops

about 10 scoops

Prerequisite Skills Inventory

Item	Standard	Common Error
1	MAFS.1.NBT.2.2b	May miscount the number of tens and ones
2	MAFS.1.NBT.2.2b	May confuse the tens place and the ones place
3	MAFS.1.NBT.2.2b	May draw the incorrect number of tens or ones
4	MAFS.1.NBT.2.2a	May group the objects incorrectly
5	MAFS.1.NBT.2.2a	May not understand that 10 ones are equal to 1 ten
6	MAFS.1.NBT.2.3	May confuse the symbols < and >
7, 9	MAFS.1.OA.3.6	May subtract incorrectly
8, 10	MAFS.1.OA.2.3	May add incorrectly
11	MAFS.1.OA.3.6	May not recognize related facts
12	MAFS.1.OA.3.6	May not realize how addition and subtraction are related
13	MAFS.1.OA.3.6	May not understand how to use the strategy *doubles plus one*
14	MAFS.1.OA.3.6	May not understand how to use the strategy *doubles plus one*
15	MAFS.1.OA.2.3	May add incorrectly
16	MAFS.1.OA.3.6	May not understand how to use the strategy *make a ten* to subtract
17	MAFS.1.NBT.3.6	May subtract multiples of 10 incorrectly
18	MAFS.1.OA.2.3	May not recognize that they can combine 4 + 6 to make a ten

Prerequisite Skills Inventory

Item	Standard	Common Error
19	MAFS.1.NBT.3.4	May forget to regroup.
20	MAFS.1.NBT.3.4	May not understand how to count on multiples of ten
21	MAFS.1.MD.2.3	May not write the time correctly
22	MAFS.1.MD.2.3	May transpose the minute and hour hand
23	MAFS.1.MD.2.3	May draw clock hands incorrectly
24	MAFS.1.MD.3.4	May incorrectly count the data points in a category
25	MAFS.1.MD.3.4	May incorrectly count the total number of data points
26	MAFS.1.MD.3.4	May not understand how to compare quantities shown on a graph
27, 28	MAFS.1.MD.1.a.c	May not measure length correctly using nonstandard units
29	MAFS.1.MD.1.1	May not understand how to order objects by length using the terms *shortest* and *longest*
30	MAFS.1.MD.1.1	May not understand how to order lengths using indirect measures
31	MAFS.1.G.1.2	May have difficulty combining three-dimensional shapes into a composite figure
32	MAFS.1.G.1.2	May have difficulty combining two-dimensional shapes into a composite figure
33	MAFS.1.G.1.3	May not be able to identify the number of equal shares

Beginning-of-Year/Middle-of-Year/End-of-Year Test

Item	Lesson	Standard	Common Error	Intervene with
1	3.5	MAFS.2.OA.2.2	May not understand the term *related fact*	R—3.5
2	3.9	MAFS.2.OA.1.1	May use an incorrect number sentence to solve	R—3.9
3	3.4	MAFS.2.OA.2.2	May not add three addends correctly	R—3.4
4	6.8	MAFS.2.NBT.2.7	May not reduce the number in the hundreds column after regrouping	R—6.8
5	6.5	MAFS.2.NBT.2.7	May incorrectly regroup ones to tens or tens to hundreds	R—6.5
6	6.10	MAFS.2.NBT.2.7	May not regroup correctly when there is a 0 in the tens	R—6.10
7	8.4	MAFS.2.MD.1.1	May not line up the edge of the ruler when measuring	R—8.4
8	8.9	MAFS.2.MD.4.9	May have difficulty reading a line plot	R—8.9
9	8.7	MAFS.2.MD.1.3	May have difficulty estimating length in feet	R—8.7
10	8.8	MAFS.2.MD.1.1	May not understand the purposes of different measuring tools	R—8.8
11	1.1	MAFS.2.OA.3.3	May not understand the meaning of *even* and *odd*	R—1.1
12	1.3	MAFS.2.NBT.1.3	May not know the value of a digit in the ones or tens place	R—1.3
13	1.5	MAFS.2.NBT.1.3	May not understand that a number can be written in different ways	R—1.5
14	1.9	MAFS.2.NBT.1.2	May not be able to count by tens or hundreds	R—1.9
15	11.1	MAFS.2.G.1.1	May not be able to identify three-dimensional shapes	R—11.1
16	11.3	MAFS.2.G.1.1	May not be able to identify two-dimensional shapes	R—11.3
17	11.5	MAFS.2.G.1.1	May not understand how to sort shapes according to the number of sides and vertices	R—11.5

Key: R—Reteach

Child's Name _____ Date _____

Beginning-of-Year/Middle-of-Year/End-of-Year Test

Item	Lesson	Standard	Common Error	Intervene with
18	11.9	MAFS.2.G.1.3	May not be able to identify a half, a third, or a fourth of a shape	R—11.9
19	3.6A	MAFS.2.OA.1.a	May find an incorrect value on one side of the equation	R—3.6A
20	4.11	MAFS.2.NBT.2.6	May forget to add the third addend	R—4.11
21	4.1	MAFS.2.NBT.2.6	May break apart ones incorrectly	R—4.1
22	4.7	MAFS.2.NBT.2.5	May add incorrectly	R—4.7
23	10.2	MAFS.2.MD.4.10	May misread the picture graph	R—10.2
24	10.3	MAFS.2.MD.4.10	May not understand how to complete a row of a picture graph	R—10.3
25	10.1	MAFS.2.MD.4	May not know that there are 5 tallies in each bundle	R—10.1
26	10.4	MAFS.2.MD.4.10	May misread the bar graph	R—10.4
27	2.5	MAFS.2.NBT.1.1	May not correctly identify the place value of the digits	R—2.5
28	2.7	MAFS.2.NBT.1.3	May not recognize a number in expanded form	R—2.7
29	2.10	MAFS.2.NBT.2.8	May not continue the pattern correctly	R—2.10
30	2.12	MAFS.2.NBT.1.4	May not know how to use the $<$, $>$, and $=$ symbols	R—2.12
31	7.3	MAFS.2.MD.3.8.b	May not be able to determine the value of a collection of coins	R—7.3
32	7.5	MAFS.2.MD.3.8.b	May not be able to identify coins that have a value of one dollar	R—7.5
33	7.11	MAFS.2.MD.3.7	May not understand A.M. and P.M.	R—7.11
34	5.1	MAFS.2.NBT.2.5	May break apart the ones incorrectly	R—5.1

Key: R—Reteach

Child's Name _____ Date _____

Beginning-of-Year/Middle-of-Year/End-of-Year Test

Item	Lesson	Standard	Common Error	Intervene with
35	5.10	MAFS.2.OA.1.1	May not understand how to write a number sentence to represent the problem	R—5.10
36	5.11	MAFS.2.OA.1.1	May forget to complete all the steps to solve the problem	R—5.11
37	5.6	MAFS.2.NBT.2.5	May not understand when to regroup	R—5.6
38	9.5	MAFS.2.MD.1.2	May not understand the relationship between a centimeter and a meter	R—9.5
39	9.3	MAFS.2.MD.1.1	May not line up the end of the object with the 0 mark on the centimeter ruler	R—9.3
40	9.7	MAFS.2.MD.1.4	May perform the wrong operation when solving a problem about comparing lengths	R—9.7

Key: R—Reteach

Chapter 1 Test

Item	Lesson	Standard	Content Focus	Intervene With
1	1.1	MAFS.2.OA.3.3	Classify numbers as even or odd.	R—1.1
2	1.2	MAFS.2.OA.3.3	Represent an even number.	R—1.2
3	1.3	MAFS.2.NBT.1.3	Identify the value of a digit in a 2-digit number.	R—1.3
4	1.1	MAFS.2.OA.3.3	Identify even and odd numbers.	R—1.1
5	1.9	MAFS.2.NBT.1.2	Count by 10s.	R—1.9
6	1.8	MAFS.2.NBT.1.2	Count by 1s and 2s.	R—1.8
7	1.4	MAFS.2.NBT.1.3	Write 2-digit numbers in expanded form.	R—1.4
8	1.3	MAFS.2.NBT.1.3	Write 2-digit numbers in standard form.	R—1.3
9	1.8	MAFS.2.NBT.1.2	Count by 5s.	R—1.8
10	1.7	MAFS.2.NBT.1.3	Use combinations of tens and ones to represent a 2-digit number.	R—1.7
11	1.6	MAFS.2.NBT.1.3	Use place value to find equivalent representations.	R—1.6

Key: R—Reteach

Child's Name _____ Date _____

Chapter 2 Test

Item	Lesson	Standard	Content Focus	Intervene With
1	2.1	MAFS.2.NBT.1.1a, MAFS.2.NBT.1.1b	Identify 10 tens as equivalent to 100.	**R**—2.1
2	2.2	MAFS.2.NBT.1.1	Apply place value concepts to solve problems.	**R**—2.2
3	2.9	MAFS.2.NBT.2.8	Identify 10 more, 100 less.	**R**—2.9
4	2.10	MAFS.2.NBT.2.8	Use place value to identify and extend counting patterns.	**R**—2.10
5	2.12	MAFS.2.NBT.1.4	Compare 3-digit numbers using >, =, and <.	**R**—2.12
6	2.4	MAFS.2.NBT.1.3	Write 3-digit numbers in word form and expanded form.	**R**—2.4
7	2.7	MAFS.2.NBT.1.3	Identify different ways to represent a number.	**R**—2.7
8	2.3	MAFS.2.NBT.1.1	Use place value to identify the values of digits.	**R**—2.3
9	2.8	MAFS.2.NBT.1.3	Use a model to represent 3-digit numbers.	**R**—2.8
10	2.11	MAFS.2.NBT.1.4	Use a model to solve problems using number comparisons.	**R**—2.11
11	2.5	MAFS.2.NBT.1.1	Use place to identify the values of digits.	**R**—2.5
12	2.6	MAFS.2.NBT.1.3	Write a 3-digit number in word form.	**R**—2.6

Key: R—Reteach

Chapter 3 Test

Item	Lesson	Standard	Content Focus	Intervene With
1	3.4	MAFS.2.OA.2.2	Add 3 addends.	R—3.4
2	3.1	MAFS.2.OA.2.2	Identify doubles facts.	R—3.1
3	3.7	MAFS.2.OA.2.2	Use a tens fact to subtract.	R—3.7
4	3.3	MAFS.2.OA.2.2	Make a ten to find the sum.	R—3.3
5	3.11	MAFS.2.OA.3.4	Find the number of objects in an array using repeated addition.	R—3.11
6	3.10	MAFS.2.OA.3.4	Model equal groups of objects to find the total number.	R—3.10
7	3.6A	MAFS.2.OA.1.a	Solve for the unknown number in a number sentence.	R—3.6A
8	3.5	MAFS.2.OA.2.2	Represent a problem using a drawing and a number sentence.	R—3.5
9	3.2	MAFS.2.OA.2.2	Represent an addition problem using a number sentence.	R—3.2
10	3.6	MAFS.2.OA.2.2	Practice subtraction facts.	R—3.6
11	3.10	MAFS.2.OA.3.4	Solve a problem involving equal groups.	R—3.10
12	3.9	MAFS.2.OA.1.1	Represent a subtraction problem using a number sentence.	R—3.9

Key: R—Reteach

Chapter 4 Test

Item	Lesson	Standard	Content Focus	Intervene With
1	4.9	MAFS.2.OA.1.1	Use a model and number sentence to solve an addition problem.	R—4.9
2	4.11	MAFS.2.NBT.2.6	Add 3 numbers.	R—4.11
3	4.10	MAFS.2.OA.1.1	Use a number sentence to solve an addition problem.	R—4.10
4	4.6	MAFS.2.NBT.2.5	Add 2-digit numbers.	R—4.6
5	4.5	MAFS.2.NBT.2.5	Model and record 2-digit addition.	R—4.5
6	4.8	MAFS.2.NBT.2.5	Add 2-digit numbers using mental math.	R—4.8
7	4.9	MAFS.2.OA.1.1	Add 2-digit numbers.	R—4.9
8	4.12	MAFS.2.NBT.2.6	Add 4 numbers.	R—4.12
9	4.3	MAFS.2.NBT.2.5	Break apart addends to add 2-digit numbers.	R—4.3
10	4.7	MAFS.2.NBT.2.5	Decide whether a sum is greater than or less than 100.	R—4.7
11	4.1	MAFS.2.NBT.2.5	Find equivalent ways to write a sum.	R—4.1
12	4.11A	MAFS.2.OA.1.a	Solve for the unknown number in an equation.	R—4.11A

Key: R—Reteach

Child's Name _____ Date _____

Chapter 5 Test

Item	Lesson	Standard	Content Focus	Intervene With
1	5.5	MAFS.2.NBT.2.5	Determine whether regrouping is necessary when subtracting.	R—5.5
2	5.8	MAFS.2.NBT.2.5	Use a number line to add to find a difference.	R—5.8
3	5.9	MAFS.2.OA.1.1	Use a bar model to solve a subtraction problem.	R—5.9
4	5.1	MAFS.2.NBT.2.5	Break apart ones to subtract.	R—5.1
5	5.2	MAFS.2.NBT.2.5	Break apart a number to subtract.	R—5.2
6	5.7	MAFS.2.NBT.2.5	Rewrite a subtraction sentence in vertical form.	R—5.7
7	5.11	MAFS.2.OA.1.1	Use bar models to solve a multistep problem.	R—5.11
8	5.5	MAFS.2.NBT.2.5	Record subtraction with regrouping.	R—5.5
9	5.5	MAFS.2.NBT.2.5	Record subtraction without regrouping.	R—5.5
10	5.6	MAFS.2.NBT.2.5	Subtract with regrouping.	R—5.6
11	5.9	MAFS.2.OA.1.1	Use subtraction to solve a word problem.	R—5.9
12	5.3	MAFS.2.NBT.2.5	Model regrouping in subtraction.	R—5.3
13	5.10	MAFS.2.OA.1.1	Write an equation to solve a subtraction problem.	R—5.10
14	5.4	MAFS.2.NBT.2.5, MAFS.2.NBT.2.9	Model and record regrouping in subtraction.	R—5.4

Key: R—Reteach

Child's Name _____ Date _____

Chapter 6 Test

Item	Lesson	Standard	Content Focus	Intervene With
1	6.8	MAFS.2.NBT.2.7	Regroup hundreds to subtract.	R—6.8
2	6.6	MAFS.2.NBT.2.7	Subtract 3-digit numbers without regrouping.	R—6.6
3	6.2	MAFS.2.NBT.2.7	Break apart 3-digit addends.	R—6.2
4	6.1	MAFS.2.NBT.2.7	Draw to represent 3-digit addition.	R—6.1
5	6.9	MAFS.2.NBT.2.7	Regroup hundreds and tens to subtract.	R—6.9
6	6.9	MAFS.2.NBT.2.7	Regroup hundreds and tens to subtract.	R—6.9
7	6.10	MAFS.2.NBT.2.7	Regroup with zeros to subtract.	R—6.10
8	6.2	MAFS.2.NBT.2.7	Break apart 3-digit addends.	R—6.2
9	6.7	MAFS.2.NBT.2.7	Regroup tens to subtract.	R—6.7
10	6.5	MAFS.2.NBT.2.7	Regroup ones and tens to add.	R—6.5

Key: R—Reteach

Child's Name _____ Date _____

Chapter 7 Test

Item	Lesson	Standard	Content Focus	Intervene With
1	7.7	MAFS.2.MD.3.8	Select combinations of bills and coins with a given value.	R—7.7
2	7.11	MAFS.2.MD.3.7	Tell time from a clock as a.m. or p.m. based on the problem scenario.	R—7.11
3	7.5A	MAFS.2.MD.3.8	Use addition to solve a problem involving money.	R—7.5A
4	7.5	MAFS.2.MD.3.8	Count a collection of coins and compare to $1.00.	R—7.5
5	7.9	MAFS.2.MD.3.7	Tell time to the nearest 5 minutes.	R—7.9
6	7.10	MAFS.2.MD.3.7	Use different ways to express time.	R—7.10
7	7.6	MAFS.2.MD.3.8	Count a collection of a bill and coins with a total greater than $1.00.	R—7.6
8	7.7A	MAFS.2.MD.3.8.a, MAFS.2.MD.3.8.c	Find the total value for a set of bills.	R—7.7A
9	7.8	MAFS.2.MD.3.7	Tell time to the hour and half hour.	R—7.8
10	7.3A	MAFS.2.MD.3.8.d	Relate the values of different coins to each other.	R—7.3A
11	7.4	MAFS.2.MD.3.8	Show an amount using coins.	R—7.4

Key: R—Reteach

Child's Name _____ Date _____

Chapter 8 Test

Item	Lesson	Standard	Content Focus	Intervene With
1	8.8	MAFS.2.MD.1.1	Choose a tool and explain.	R—8.8
2	8.5	MAFS.2.MD.2.5, MAFS.2.MD.2.6	Relate addition to length and use a number line diagram.	R—8.5
3	8.4	MAFS.2.MD.1.1	Use a ruler to measure length to the nearest inch.	R—8.4
4	8.1	MAFS.2.MD.1.1	Measure length with an inch model.	R—8.1
5	8.9	MAFS.2.MD.4.9	Use a line plot.	R—8.9
6	8.6	MAFS.2.MD.1.2	Select inches or feet as the correct units for given measures.	R—8.6
7	8.3	MAFS.2.MD.1.3	Estimate length using an inch model.	R—8.3
8	8.7A	MAFS.2.MD.1.3	Estimate length in yards.	R—8.7A
9	8.7	MAFS.2.MD.1.3	Estimate length in feet.	R—8.7

Key: **R**—Reteach

Chapter 9 Test

Item	Lesson	Standard	Content Focus	Intervene With
1	9.1	MAFS.2.MD.1.1	Measure length using a centimeter model.	R—9.1
2	9.2	MAFS.2.MD.1.3	Use known lengths to estimate unknown lengths.	R—9.2
3	9.4	MAFS.2.MD.2.5, MAFS.2.MD.2.6	Use a number line diagram and addition to solve a length problem.	R—9.4
4	9.5	MAFS.2.MD.1.2	Select centimeters or meters as the correct unit for given measures.	R—9.5
5	9.6	MAFS.2.MD.1.3	Estimate length in meters.	R—9.6
6	9.7	MAFS.2.MD.1.4	Measure and compare lengths of two objects.	R—9.7
7	9.4	MAFS.2.MD.2.5, MAFS.2.MD.2.6	Use a number line diagram and subtraction to solve a length problem.	R—9.4
8	9.3	MAFS.2.MD.1.1	Measure length to the nearest centimeter.	R—9.3

Key: R—Reteach

Chapter 10 Test

Item	Lesson	Standard	Content Focus	Intervene With
1	10.1	MAFS.2.MD.4.10	Make a tally chart.	R—10.1
2	10.1	MAFS.2.MD.4.10	Read and interpret a tally chart.	R—10.1
3	10.1	MAFS.2.MD.4.10	Make and interpret a tally chart.	R—10.1
4	10.6	MAFS.2.MD.4.10	Make and interpret a bar graph.	R—10.6
5	10.6	MAFS.2.MD.4.10	Read and interpret a bar graph.	R—10.6
6	10.3	MAFS.2.MD.4.10	Complete a picture graph.	R—10.3
7	10.2	MAFS.2.MD.4.10	Read and interpret a picture graph.	R—10.2
8	10.2	MAFS.2.MD.4.10	Read and interpret a picture graph.	R—10.2
9	10.2	MAFS.2.MD.4.10	Read and interpret a picture graph.	R—10.2
10	10.5	MAFS.2.MD.4.10	Complete a bar graph.	R—10.5
11	10.4	MAFS.2.MD.4.10	Read and interpret a bar graph.	R—10.4
12	10.4	MAFS.2.MD.4.10	Read and interpret a bar graph.	R—10.4
13	10.4	MAFS.2.MD.4.10	Read and interpret a bar graph.	R—10.4

Key: R—Reteach

Child's Name _____ Date _____

Chapter 11 Test

Item	Lesson	Standard	Content Focus	Intervene With
1	11.1	MAFS.2.G.1.1	Match objects and three-dimensional shapes.	R—11.1
2	11.2	MAFS.2.G.1.1	Identify attributes of a rectangular prism.	R—11.2
3	11.9	MAFS.2.G.1.3	Draw to show equal parts of a two-dimensional shape.	R—11.9
4	11.11	MAFS.2.G.1.3	Draw a diagram to solve a problem about equal parts.	R—11.11
5	11.10	MAFS.2.G.1.3	Draw halves, thirds, and fourths.	R—11.10
6	11.7	MAFS.2.G.1.2	Estimate the number of tiles that cover a rectangle.	R—11.7
7	11.3	MAFS.2.G.1.1	Determine the number of cubes in a rectangular prism.	R—11.3
8	11.4	MAFS.2.G.1.1	Count sides of two-dimensional shapes to solve a problem.	R—11.4
9	11.5	MAFS.2.G.1.1	Draw two-dimensional shapes with a given number of angles.	R—11.5
10	11.8	MAFS.2.G.1.3	Identify shapes divided into thirds.	R—11.8
11	11.6	MAFS.2.G.1.1	Sort two-dimensional shapes by number of angles.	R—11.6

Key: R—Reteach

Getting Ready Test: Lessons 1–12

Item	Lesson	Common Error	Intervene with
1, 23	4	May not understand how to estimate the difference of two 2-digit numbers	**R**—p. GRR4
2, 7	1	May not understand how to use anaddition table	**R**—p. GRR1
3, 15	6	May not understand how to identify the least or greatest number	**R**—p. GRR6
4, 24	8	May not understand how to recognize equal groups of 5 and find the total number	**R**—p. GRR8
5, 13	3	May not understand how to estimate the sum of two 3-digit numbers	**R**—p. GRR3
6, 12	9	May not understand how to recognize equal groups of 10 and find the total number	**R**—p. GRR9
8, 20	5	May not understand how to estimate the difference of two 3-digit numbers.	**R**—p. GRR5
9, 16	7	May not understand how to recognize equal groups of 2 and find the total number	**R**—p. GRR7
10, 18	2	May not understand how to estimate the sum of two 2-digit numbers	**R**—p. GRR2
11, 22	10	May not understand how to find the number in each group, given the total and the number of groups	**R**—p. GRR10
14, 19	12	May not understand how to solve word problems involving equal shares	**R**—p. GRR12
17, 21	11	May not understand how to find the number of groups, given the total and the number in each group	**R**—p. GRR11

Key: R—Reteach

Child's Name _____ Date _____

Getting Ready Test: Lessons 13–20

Item	Lesson	Common Error	Intervene with
1, 5, 21	13	May confuse *1 hour before* or *1 hour after* the given time	**R**—p. GRR13
2, 11, 24	16	May not understand how to make visual connections between nonstandard units of capacity and everyday objects	**R**—p. GRR16
3, 17, 20	18	May confuse thirds and sixths	**R**—p. GRR18
4, 7, 13	14	May not understand how to use a time line to find elapsed time in hours	**R**—p. GRR14
6, 14, 19	17	May not understand how to use a line plot to solve problems	**R**—p. GRR17
8, 16, 23	15	May not understand how to subtract to find elapsed time in minutes	**R**—p. GRR15
9, 15, 22	19	May confuse fourths and eighths	**R**—p. GRR19
10, 12, 18	20	May confuse comparison symbols	**R**—p. GRR20

Key: **R**—Reteach